Bats in th~ ~

by
Shirley Tho

Illustrations by
Tessa Lovatt-Smith

Contents

School Garden Company

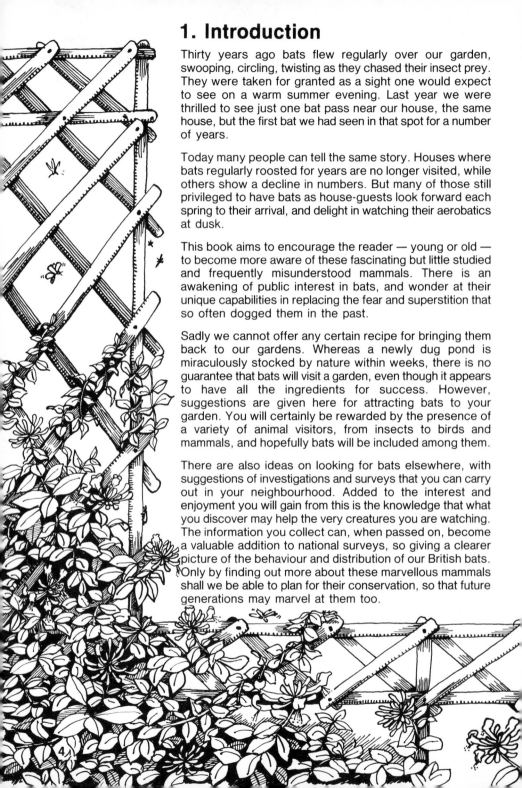

1. Introduction

Thirty years ago bats flew regularly over our garden, swooping, circling, twisting as they chased their insect prey. They were taken for granted as a sight one would expect to see on a warm summer evening. Last year we were thrilled to see just one bat pass near our house, the same house, but the first bat we had seen in that spot for a number of years.

Today many people can tell the same story. Houses where bats regularly roosted for years are no longer visited, while others show a decline in numbers. But many of those still privileged to have bats as house-guests look forward each spring to their arrival, and delight in watching their aerobatics at dusk.

This book aims to encourage the reader — young or old — to become more aware of these fascinating but little studied and frequently misunderstood mammals. There is an awakening of public interest in bats, and wonder at their unique capabilities in replacing the fear and superstition that so often dogged them in the past.

Sadly we cannot offer any certain recipe for bringing them back to our gardens. Whereas a newly dug pond is miraculously stocked by nature within weeks, there is no guarantee that bats will visit a garden, even though it appears to have all the ingredients for success. However, suggestions are given here for attracting bats to your garden. You will certainly be rewarded by the presence of a variety of animal visitors, from insects to birds and mammals, and hopefully bats will be included among them.

There are also ideas on looking for bats elsewhere, with suggestions of investigations and surveys that you can carry out in your neighbourhood. Added to the interest and enjoyment you will gain from this is the knowledge that what you discover may help the very creatures you are watching. The information you collect can, when passed on, become a valuable addition to national surveys, so giving a clearer picture of the behaviour and distribution of our British bats. Only by finding out more about these marvellous mammals shall we be able to plan for their conservation, so that future generations may marvel at them too.

2. Facts and Fantasies

For generations past bats have been persecuted, mistrusted and misunderstood throughout many parts of the world. Yet with very few exceptions they are useful to man. All British bats are insect eaters, consuming such huge numbers that in some countries they are actively encouraged in order to keep down insect pests. In other countries some bats are important because they pollinate or spread the seeds of many commercially important plants such as peaches, bananas and almonds.

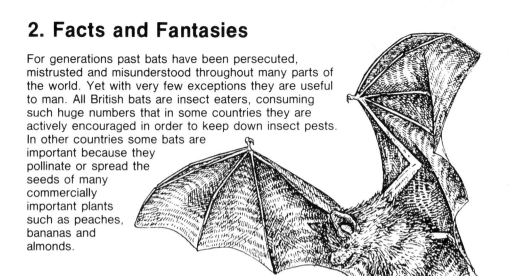

Serotine

Despite this, myths about bats are still believed, modern horror stories and films feature them, and fiction is still quoted as fact. Although the media is often blamed, this fear goes back generations, before the days of newsprint or camera. The Chinese are one of the few nations to recognise bats for the beneficial creatures they really are, including them in their textile and ceramic designs as bringers of good fortune. How can so many people get the wrong idea?

Bats are creatures of the night, with seemingly uncanny powers of finding their prey under the cover of darkness. Their unnerving acrobatic flight at dusk, their secretive habits, their magical awakening from death-like hibernation in winter, must all have helped link them with other unexplained mysteries of the night. Over 2,000 years ago Aesop attempted to explain their strange life-style in one of his Fables, probably basing it on an even earlier story. He told of a battle between the birds and the beasts in which the bat was uncertain with whom to side; as a mouse with the beasts or, because of his wings, as a bird. Finally the bat was rejected by both, and doomed to spend his life hiding from the birds during the daytime, and flying out of reach of the beasts at night.

So, what is a bat?
Bats are mammals, the group of animals which have fur or hair on their bodies and give birth to live young. Like all mammals, from cats and elephants to whales and humans, they suckle their young on milk and care for them until they become independent.

There are nearly a thousand species of bat, almost a quarter of all the different mammal species. They are to be found all over the world with the exception of the Arctic and Antarctic. Whilst the majority eat insects, there are also vegetarian bats eating fruit or flowers, and bats-of-prey taking fish, frogs and even other mammals.

*Life-size
Pipistrelle*

British Bats

Being an island and quite far north, Britain has only fourteen breeding species, though a fifteenth also bred here until recently. Most may be found on the warm south coast, with only four species regularly found as far north as Scotland. The two horseshoe bats belong to the family *Rhinolophidae*, while the other thirteen are all members of the family *Vespertilionidae*, the Vesper or evening bats. If the variations between them come as a surprise, we should remind ourselves that the dog family includes such dissimilar animals as the fox, the wolf and the jackal, as well as the many breeds of our own domestic dog. Just as all these share common features while being very·different in character and habit, so each bat species has its own characteristics, living and feeding in diverse ways, yet all very obviously bats.

BATS RESIDENT IN BRITAIN

Family	Species	Distribution
Horseshoe bats *Rhinolophidae*	Greater horseshoe bat *(Rhinolophus ferrumequinum)*	S Wales, SW England, very rare
	Lesser horseshoe bat *(R. hipposideros)*	Wales and SW England, rare
Vesper bats *Vespertilionidae*	Whiskered bat *(Myotis mystacinus)*	England, commoner in west and north
	Brandt's bat *(M. brandtii)*	As above, but less common
	Daubenton's bat *(M. daubentonii)*	Throughout Britain
	Natterer's bat *(M. nattereri)*	Throughout Britain
	Bechstein's bat *(M. bechsteinii)*	Parts of S England, very rare
	Mouse-eared bat *(M. myotis)*	One specimen remaining (January 1989)
	Pipistrelle *(Pipistrellus pipistrellus)*	Common everywhere
	Serotine *(Eptisecus serotinus)*	S and SE Britain
	Noctule *(Nyctalus noctula)*	Mainly England and Wales
	Leisler's bat *(N. leisleri)*	England and Ireland, rare in England
	Brown long-eared bat *(Plecotus auritus)*	Widely distributed throughout Britain
	Grey long-eared bat *(P. austriacus)*	Very rare, only in S England
	Barbastelle *(Barbastella barbastellus)*	Very rare, no colonies known

3. What makes bats seem so different?

Wings in the darkness

The ability to fly sets bats apart from all other mammals. *Chiroptera*, the name given to the whole order of bats, means 'hand-wing', and the structure of their hand and arm is remarkably like our own. Just as you can move your arms independently of each other, a bat by bending its elbows and stretching open its hands is able to manoeuvre in the air, and change the curve of the wing to adjust speed.

Imagine the bones of your fingers growing to the full length of your body; this will give some idea of the relative size of a bat's wing. A membrane of almost hairless skin joins the fingers and then connects to the ankle and beyond to the tail. Compared with a bird this provides a very large wing area, and a bat seen in the hand is always much smaller than expected. A pipistrelle, our smallest and commonest bat, fits easily into a matchbox when its wings are folded (as shown on page 6).

Different species have differently shaped wings to suit the way they catch and eat their food. The tail is usually curled under, with the membrane enclosing it being stiffened by the calcar. A bat at rest normally hang by its toes, out of the way of predators, though it may also use its thumbs for hanging or climbing.

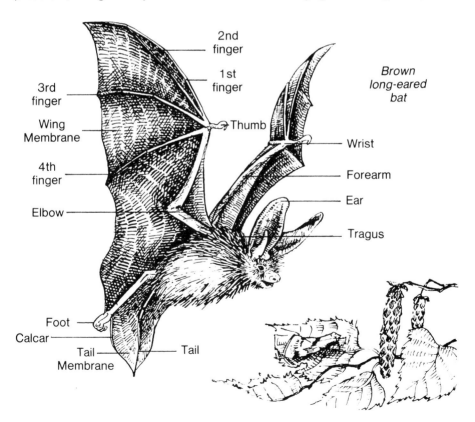

2nd finger
1st finger
3rd finger
Wing Membrane
4th finger
Elbow
Thumb
Brown long-eared bat
Wrist
Forearm
Ear
Tragus
Foot
Calcar
Tail Membrane
Tail

Seeing with sound — Echolocation

It is a reflection on our technological age that though many people are surprised at some of the more basic and long-understood facts about bats, most are aware that bats employ a highly sophisticated method of finding their prey using ultrasonic sound. However, until some fifty years ago scientists were baffled by the bats' ability to fly and feed by night. As early as the eighteenth century it was proved that their ears rather than their eyes were essential for this, but why, as they were so silent? Only in 1938, using sonar equipment developed in World War 1, were the very high frequency sounds emitted by bats first 'heard' by man.

British bats produce a wide range of sounds, patterns and frequencies varying with species, as they search for their insect prey. The horseshoe bat beams sound out through its nose with the aid of a horseshoe-shaped dish; the long-eared bat either whispers quietly or listens to sounds made by the moth's wings, while the high-flying noctule shouts through its open mouth as it echolocates at the sound level of a pneumatic drill. As light reflects from objects back to our eyes, enabling us to recognise colour, shape, texture and much more, so clicks and shouts produced by the bat bounce back, giving information about its surroundings. Bats have been developing this sytem for at least fifty million years, so it is hardly surprising that as newcomers to the technology, there is much that we still have to learn about the way they use it.

Children or others with acute hearing are occasionally aware of some of the lowest of the clicks used in echolocation. In contrast, audible sounds of squeaking and chattering are often easily heard from outside nursery roosts. Usually these are noisiest just before evening emergence. Baby bats, if separated from their mother, have a high-pitched but audible call.

*Noctule bat
echolocating*

4. It's a Bat's Life

Although many people think of bats as social animals, living in large groups, this is only part of the picture. Their lives are surprisingly complicated, behaviour and habits changing with the seasons.

All our British bats eat insects, and the pattern of their lives is woven around the availability of insects and the best way to conserve the energy they gain from eating them. So the weather, which directly affects insect activity and populations, has therefore a crucial effect on all our bats. As a result, variations in behaviour may be found not only between species, but within the same species in different parts of Britain and from one year to the next.

Spring and summer

During spring pregnant females gather in small groups which then join up at a maternity or nursery roost-site. They choose a warm place and form clusters so as to conserve energy whilst the unborn baby is developing. In June or July they give birth, usually to a single young. The tiny baby, at first blind and hairless with wings not fully formed, is suckled frequently and cared for tenderly. Unless changing roost sites, the mother normally hangs the baby up when she goes out to feed, and is gradually able to leave it for longer intervals. Within days its eyes are open, and its fur starts to grow; by the end of the second week it is starting to stretch its wings.

Between about three and five weeks of age the young start flying. Watching their clockwork-like flight in these early stages, one can almost imagine their look of concentration! Little is known of what is taught by the mothers, but batwatchers may notice bats in pairs, one smaller than the other, giving the impression of flying in formation, as they dodge and manoeuvre after their insect prey. The mothers never catch insects for their young, but suckling ceases after about 30 to 40 days when the young are capable of feeding independently.

What of the males meanwhile? Theirs is a much less sociable summer. Roosting singly or in small groups, they frequently become torpid during the day, warming up only at night in order to feed. There may be occasional visits to the nursery roost-site, but species vary and many questions as to their behaviour remain unanswered.

Autumn

In autumn the bats split into smaller groups again, and mating takes place from September. Soon they start to prepare for winter hibernation. They feed well, increasing weight by about a third, becoming torpid for longer periods, and waking less often, so that settling into hibernation is a gradual process rather than a sudden change.

Winter

In a cool place, such as a cave or tunnel, their temperature drops to nearly match that of their surroundings and breathing and heartbeat slow down. The animal may give the appearance of being dead. As conditions change they still occasionally wake even in midwinter, to feed, drink or urinate, or to move if necessary to another site. However, unplanned arousals, as a result of disturbance, use up vital stored energy and may prevent survival until spring, especially if warm weather is late in coming.

5. What do bats need to survive?

There are two basic necessities of life to bats. They need plenty of food, and a choice of places to roost.

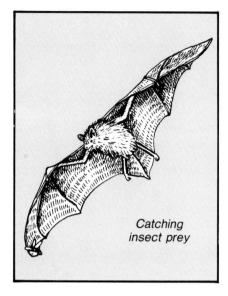

Catching
insect prey

That sounds simple enough, but these are much more complicated demands than they first appear. The number and variety of their insect prey depends on season and weather as well as many environmental factors. Numerous roost-sites may be used by a single bat during the year, different conditions being looked for at different times, so it can all become rather involved. To see how we may create or improve conditions for at least some parts of the jigsaw we need to look more closely at their requirements.

Food

Flight uses up a great deal of energy, so bats need to catch many insects to make it worthwhile hunting them. They may consume as much as a third of their body weight in one night, but on a poor night the catch will be much less. Insect activity decreases noticeably when the temperature falls below 10°C, and also when it is raining or a strong wind is blowing. On such nights bats may not emerge at all, or only for a short time.

Insect densities are highest around dusk, a fact which bats as night hunters take full advantage of, though they do occasionally also feed during the day. Although some species may land to take beetles, and others like the long-eared bat will pick moths from leaves, most of their prey is taken in flight. Having located the insect of their choice, they may catch it directly in their mouth or use their wing or tail membrane as a scoop and pass the prey to their mouth, sometimes getting a better grip by pushing the head into the tail membrane. Some bats eat their prey on the wing, others return to a perch to consume it.

The various species of bat have different feeding strategies and food preferences, but all will return to favoured places and follow traditional feeding paths where they have previously been successful. The abundance of insects is affected by the presence of water, the vegetation, and the degree of shelter in the vicinity. Native broad-leaved trees such as the oak, ash and silver birch, are food plants for many insects. Winged insects also gather in the shelter offered by tall hedges, enclosed gardens and churchyards. Even some insects that lay their eggs on the grasses and wild flowers of meadows where the larvae feed, spend much of their time as adults in woodland sites. So the edge of woodland, or somewhere offering similar conditions, is a favourite place for bats to forage. In order to benefit bats in our gardens, we need to try and reproduce such habitats to attract their insect prey.

Roosting Sites

Why do bats hang upside down? With front limbs adapted for flying, their tiny clawed hind feet are much the more suitable for hanging. By roosting high up, a whole range of sites is available to them out of reach of most predators.

Any place a bat rests is known technically as a roost. Bats add no extra material to their roost sites or make any sort of nest, yet it is known that the same bat may return to the same crack at the same time of year for many years. They certainly have favourite spots which they recognise and use regularly.

However, the problem is that one site is not enough. Different types of roost sites are preferred according to species, sex, age and condition, and even then there are different requirements according to weather and the time of year. Generally speaking, in the summer somewhere warm is needed, especially by females in their nursery roosts, while during the winter they seek cool, humid and undisturbed environments in which to hibernate.

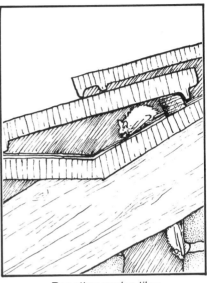

Roosting under tiles

Originally all bats were cave or tree dwelling animals. When Britain was covered by forest, long before man appeared on the scene, woodland bats found life much easier. Fossil remains reveal that Bechstein's bat was common, though now it is rarely recorded more than a few times a year. With the arrival of man the toolmaker, mines and quarries were added to the natural cave systems, especially in the south-west. Cave bats such as the greater horseshoe found conditions here were ideal, and flourished.

While the widespread clearance of woodland worked to the detriment of bat species heavily dependant on trees for their roosts, those able to adapt to man-made structures gained an advantage. The older a building, so the greater the number of species likely to be present, as in some of our castles and stately homes. Every one of our 15 species in Britain has been found in houses, but some, such as the noctule, still much prefer trees. It is clear however that buildings, bridges and walls are very important to several species.

But it is the little pipistrelle that has most fully taken over our homes. It enjoys creeping into tight spots, behind hanging tiles and slates, under barge boarding, soffit boards and roof tiles. It even seems to prefer modern buildings, and is by far the most abundant bat.

Yet even the pipistrelle, our commonest bat, has declined alarmingly. Why?

Bats need friends

Along with clouds of butterflies and flower-filled meadows, so 'swarms of bats' only exist in people's memories in most parts of Britain today. Long-term studies show a startling reduction in numbers and recent colony surveys indicate that the decline continues.

Although much is still neither known nor understood about the exact requirements of different species, it is clear that changes in our environment have reduced both feeding and roosting sites, to the detriment of bats.

Woodlands have been felled to make way for housing and other development, hedges uprooted to enlarge fields, dead and mature trees cleared for safety or tidiness, and motorways carved out of rural areas. Not only are there fewer trees available for roosting, but also traditional flight lines and shelter belts, where bats have foraged in the past, have been fragmented.

Many river banks have been cleared of overhanging trees and emergent vegetation, marshy areas have been drained, and countless ponds filled in, impairing the freshwater habitat on which so many insects depend. Numerous aerial insects lay their eggs in water, where the earlier part of their life cycle takes place, and these can be further reduced by agricultural run-off and industrial discharge into rivers.

Traditional farmland used to offer a rotation of crops together with pastures and meadows, so producing a variety of insects through the seasons. Moths, butterflies and beetles were plentiful in the meadow, craneflies and dungbeetles in the pastures, gnats and midges over the farm pond. Today agriculture is more often based on large areas given over to single crops, or to intensive livestock farming. Flower-rich hay meadows have been replaced with fields of non-native grass supporting few insects. Pesticides and other chemicals, used extensively to support such farming, further reduce the number of insects, while those remaining may carry low levels of pesticides. When bats eat large numbers of these, toxic chemicals can build up to lethal concentrations and are especially dangerous during hibernation.

Remedial timber treatment for woodboring beetles and fungi has killed many bats. Pesticides can be absorbed through the skin of a roosting bat, inhaled as vapour or ingested as it grooms. Most of the more lethal chemicals have now been withdrawn from the market, but some are still being used, despite the availability of pesticides which are safer for all mammals.
Hibernation sites too are threatened as caves, mines and tunnels are blocked in the name of safety, opened to tourists, or disturbed by the careless explorer.

Bats in Britain are at the limit of their range. With so many other pressures, they are particularly vulnerable to extremes of weather. Extended winters and cold summers can reduce the numbers and species of insects available just when they are most needed.

6. Bats in the garden

Since 1981 all British bats and their roosts have been protected by law. An explanation of how this can affect householders is given on page 26. Over the wider scene, it has led to a complete change in attitude for many people.

Thanks to concerted efforts by batworkers at all levels, and positive input by the media, the public generally is much more aware of bats. Attitudes based on ignorance and misunderstanding are increasingly being replaced by a fascination for their lifestyle and a very real concern for their future.

How can we help in bat conservation?

We can supply pools of clean water and create or improve habitats that support a wide range of insects. We can provide quiet sheltered areas and increase options for roosting.

However small a garden, careful planning **will** increase its value to wildlife. Decide, according to its size, what you can reasonably offer. Plants provide the basic platform for animal life. The greater the variety of **suitable** plants, the larger the menu not only for plant-eaters, but also in turn for associated animals, including birds, bats and other small mammals. Make an overall plan of your garden, bearing in mind its vertical structure. Varying levels present a wider bill of fare for visitors and inhabitants, from treetop restaurant to basement cafe.

Birds have become increasingly dependent on gardens for food and nesting sites, and garden ponds are life-savers for many frogs and other amphibians. Your house and garden could provide the missing pieces in the jigsaw of a bat's seasonal needs.

Pieces in the jigsaw

Trees and shrubs

To attract bats to feed in the garden, you should create a habitat rich in insects. Before planning any changes, look at what the bats already have access to, not just in your garden, but also nearby. Try to complement what is available, for bats feed over a wide area, often many square kilometres.

The most valuable part of a woodland to bats, as with many other creatures, is the edge, where space and sunshine combine with the trees to give shelter and warmth. So even in the smallest garden try to have at least one tree or shrub. If space is limited quick growing silver birch and goat willow are ideal and play host to many insect visitors. With a little more space, try to make a bank of vegetation to give your garden a woodland edge structure.

Bear the following in mind:
   In general native trees are by far the most valuable; those introduced for their appearance are usually unattractive to our British insects.
   Beware of trees that will grow too big; instead plant shrubs such as hawthorn and field maple.
   Before felling an overgrown tree, plant a young sapling to replace it.

Use trees to screen unsightly views, but think about the direction of the shade they will cast when grown taller.
   Plant young saplings or whips, no taller than a metre, in late autumn or early spring.
   Follow the grower's instructions carefully.
   A hedge is a scaled down version of a woodland edge that can be kept manageable by clipping. It can provide a variety of species in a limited space.
   At ground level, allow fallen leaves and twigs to rot. Piles of brushwood and dead leaves are home to countless creatures which break down the vegetation and add nutrients and humus to the soil.
   Think carefully before killing anything, or clearing away dying or dead plants. Every invertebrate killed is a potential meal lost to some predator.

14

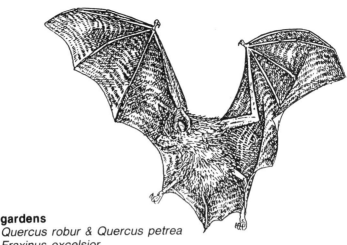

Large trees for large gardens

Oak   *Quercus robur & Quercus petrea*
Ash   *Fraxinus excelsior*

Smaller trees

Silver Birch   *Betula pendula*
Field Maple   *Acer campestre*
Hawthorn   *Crataegus monogyna* — shade tolerant, excellent for hedges
Alder   *Alnus glutinosa* — tolerant of pollution and waterlogged soils

Shrubs

Goat Willow   *Salix caprea* — coppice
Guelder Rose   *Viburnum opulus* — shade-tolerant
Hazel   *Coryllus avellana* — coppice
Blackthorn   *Prunus spinosa*
Elder   *Sambucus nigra*
Buddleia   *Buddleia davidii* — non-native but valuable, dead-head regularly to extend flowering period, or if more than one plant, clip at different times

Flowers, lawns and shelterbelts

Alongside our woodland edge, flower borders and lawns can offer food and cover to many insects. By introducing a wide range of food, in the form of nectar, seeds and fruit as well as vegetation, larvae and adults of many insect species will be catered for. This in turn makes available a wider menu for bats, with each bat species having its own food preferences. At the same time you will find the beauty and interest of your garden enhanced by butterflies, birds and many other garden visitors.

However, as bats usually feed at dusk and dawn, include a good supply of **night-scented flowers**. These release their scent as darkness falls, attracting moths and other nightflying insects to feed and so pollinate them. A bed of scented herbs too will not only bring pleasure to you and flavour to your cooking but also entice insects by their bouquet. Some of the old-fashioned cottage-garden annuals, though non-native, also attract many insects.

Numerous aerial insects spend their larval stages feeding on grass, but regularly mown lawns have little to offer them. Leave a portion of your lawn without mowing from about the middle of May and see what comes into flower. Provided you have never used weedkiller you could be surprised at what appears. Wait until the flower seeds have set before cutting, and rake up the hay afterwards, so as *not* to increase the fertility of the soil. Chemicals should never be added to the lawn.

Selections of seeds suitable for different soils are available if you would like to develop an area of meadow further, or build up wild flower collections in your borders. Information on where to obtain these can be found in Appendix B.

Shelter belts can be created by walls and fences, so encouraging concentrations of insects in the same way as hedgerows. If you have a wall or fence already, the planting of climbers will add another level to your garden structure. Fix battens when training climbing plants, so creating additional spaces for shelter. In addition to the food value of the growing plant, and the insects it attracts, this will improve the habitat for invertebrates and be available as a roosting site for bats.

Ivy is particularly valuable, producing nectar very late in the year, and providing dense shelter throughout the seasons. Honeysuckle, with its wonderful perfume at dusk, should be in every bat garden. If you have space, plant several species to flower in sequence through the summer.

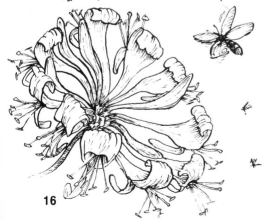

Honeysuckle

16

If there is sufficient space to plant conifers without doing so at the expense of native trees, shelter belts can be quickly formed from them, the thick vegetation producing excellent shelter in all months.

Create a sheltered corner by planning a shelter belt at two angles, running north-south and east-west. This can be formed with any combination of walls, fences, hedges or woodland edge, and will effectively allow insect concentrations to build up.

Night-scented flowers for the border
(In approximate order of flowering)

Nottingham catchfly	*Silene nutans*
Night-scented catchfly	*S. noctiflora*
Bladder campion	*S. vulgaris*
Night-scented stock	*Matthiola bicornis*
Sweet rocket	*Hesperis matronalis*
Evening primrose	*Oenothera biennis*
Tobacco plant	*Nicotiana affinis*
Cherry pie	*Heliotropum x hybridum*
Soapwort	*Spanoria officinalis*

Scented herbs

Chives	*Allium schoenoprasum*
Sage	*Salvia officinalis*
Marjoram	*Origanum vulgare*
Borage	*Borago officinalis*
Mint	*Mentha sp* — many varieties
Lemon balm	*Melissa officinalis*

Climbers

European honeysuckle	*Lonicera caprifolium* July-Nov
Italian honeysuckle	*L. Etrusca superba* July-Aug
Japanese honeysuckle	*L. japonica halliana* Aug-Oct
Honeysuckle (native)	*L. periclymenum* July-Aug
White jasmine	*Jasminium officinale*
Dogrose	*Rosa canina*
Sweetbriar	*R. rubiginosa*
Fieldrose	*R. arvensis*
Ivy	*Hedera helix*
Bramble — many species	

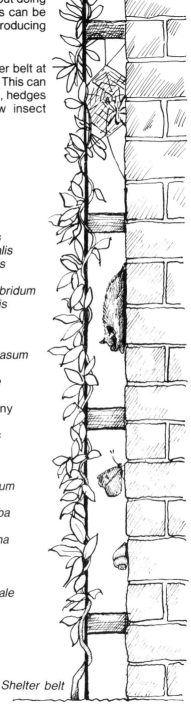

Shelter belt

Where are they?

Shown in the picture are at least 16 places where bats might roost.

How many can you find?

Ponds

Many insects, including numerous species of midges, gnats and mosquitoes, spend the first part of their lives in freshwater, only emerging to become airborne as adults. As one pipistrelle may eat over 3,000 such insects in a night, a pond is an important part of any garden designed to attract bats.

If concerned for the safety of small children, make a pond in the normal way and fill it in to form a marsh. Later, when the family can cope with open water, dig a hole in the middle. An old leaking concrete pond can also easily be converted to a marsh.

The simplest and most successful way of creating a pond is by using a flexible liner. Mark the shape out with a rope and live with it for a while before making a final decision. Make it as large as possible within limitations of space and cost. With a good surface area and space around it, you may have the joy not only of bats feeding over it but also of them drinking as they fly, scooping up water with their open mouths.

Nature's stocking of ponds is amazingly rapid. There is usually no need to put any pond creatures in the water: just wait and watch. Whatever you do, *don't* put in goldfish, as they will eat all the creatures that you hope to encourage.

A sheltered edge, with a fence or hedge, will encourage larger densities of insects. (A companion book in this series — **Starting a wildlife pond** — gives full details).

Construction details are available elsewhere (see Appendix A), but generally speaking, bear the following points in mind:

Allow for the lining to be large enough to cover the whole of the bottom and sides plus 300mm overlap.

Make the hole at least 150mm deeper than the depth you want it to be.

Vary the depths, making one part at least 600mm deep to prevent freezing, and another very shallow.

Slope the sides gently.

Layer newspapers, old carpets, or sand inside your hole before putting the liner in place, in order to cushion it.

Put a layer of soil about 50mm deep inside your pond before filling it with water.

Trickle water in and leave for several days before planting.

Trim and bury the edge of the liner after filling with water.

The best time to plant your wetland is April or May. Use native plants, but don't dig them from the wild.

Include marginal and emergent plants at the water's edge, in addition to submerged oxygenating plants.

In time, some of the subsequent growth will need to be cleared, in order to maintain open water.

Added Attractions

Lighting-up time

We all know that insects are attracted to bright lights. Bats learn of such food sources, so by fixing a light in your garden and regularly leaving it on at dusk you may encourage bats to visit as part of their nightly foraging routine. The brighter the light, the more insects will find it, especially if placed near the pond. Mercury vapour lights are particularly attractive to insects.

A pile of logs left undisturbed in the shrubbery or a corner of the garden to rot will become home to a host of insects and other organisms. Similarly **a compost heap,** in addition to providing a good organic compost, will create a habitat for a whole community of creatures, food in turn for larger predators.

Build a rockery on the principle of drystone walling. A double sided wall, filled with stones and incorporating very little soil, can become an attractive feature as mosses and lichens colonise. Introduce wall ferns and rock plants such as stonecrop, and an ivy root at the base. The spaces will be available as roost sites for bats, as well as home for some of the invertebrates on which they prey. If walls are well capped to keep out water then more wildlife will use them. Alternatively, an earth bank faced with a dry stone wall may be more suited to your garden. Leave cavities in the centre as well as plenty of small holes in the facing.

Rock plants suitable for walls.

Ivy-leaved toadflax	*Cymbalaria muralis*	Herb Robert	*Geranium robertianum*
Wall pennywort	*Umbilicus rupestris*	Stonecrop	*Sedum acre*

A Garden Diary

Keep a log of the changes or additions you make to your garden.
Note when the plants come into flower: use these notes to help you fill gaps the following year. Regularly check your pond for colonisers. Record insects and birds, when and what they visit.

Be on the lookout in the evening, from just *before* it gets dark, for the night shift coming on. Watch for bats foraging around the edge of the trees as well as in open spaces and over water.

---

7. Somewhere to put their feet up

Bats about buildings

Houses as roosting sites are now considered essential to the continued survival of several of Britain's bat species. Bats move from site to site, sometimes even during the breeding season, though we are not clear exactly why they should do this.

Householders who would welcome them as house-guests may like to develop or incorporate features that are regularly used by bats into their own homes, though it is not always apparent whether a house **is** being used by bats. Even if it is not visited at present it is still worth providing a suitable environment. The opportunity may be taken up at some later date.

A warning. If your loft has been treated in the past with toxic chemicals, especially DDT or Dieldrin, it is better *not* to encourage bats to use the roof space as it may still be lethal to them. If future timber treatment is *really* necessary, be sure to use chemicals non – toxic to mammals. Even if there is no evidence of bats, you will be conserving it for their possible future use, and reducing hazards to the other mammals in the house – humans and pets.

If bats are known to use a house, even occasionally, seek advice from the NCC before any work is done, including repairs and building work. (See page 26). Even blocking the smallest hole may exclude or entomb them unknowingly. Avoid redecorating near roosting sites when bats are present, especially between late June and August, when females with young may be in residence.

Suggested additions and modifications

Rough-sawn weather boarding is a popular roosting place. A few boards fastened to a wall can provide shelter for a large number of bats, a southerly aspect being generally preferred.

By boxing in part of the eaves, what is virtually an elongated bat-box is made available. Several gaps, 15-20mm wide and about 200mm long, will give a choice of access points. Boarding fixed at the gable apex could also cater for bats.

Tiles with cowled apertures and ventilated ridge tiles with slits at the side are available. Designed to ventilate the roof, they can be tailored to suit bats if necessary by cutting mesh or smoothing edges. Even bat bricks have recently been marketed to ensure easier access.

If you have bats in residence, do not disturb them. See page 27 for ways of recording their activities. Your local bat group may be able to visit and confirm identification.

Bat Boxes

Bat boxes, as artificial holes, offer an additional option for bats searching for a roost site. Entrance is by way of a narrow slot underneath. The following points are based on the success of previous schemes.

1. Bats should be seen regularly in the vicinity.

2. Grouped boxes are more beneficial than single ones. Site them facing south east and south west, two to a tree.

3. Wood should be of untreated rough sawn timber, at least 20mm thick. Location is more important than design, though clusters of animals are more likely to use those with an internal volume of 10x10x10cm.

4. Position the boxes as high as is convenient, preferably 3-4 metres, unobstructed by branches.

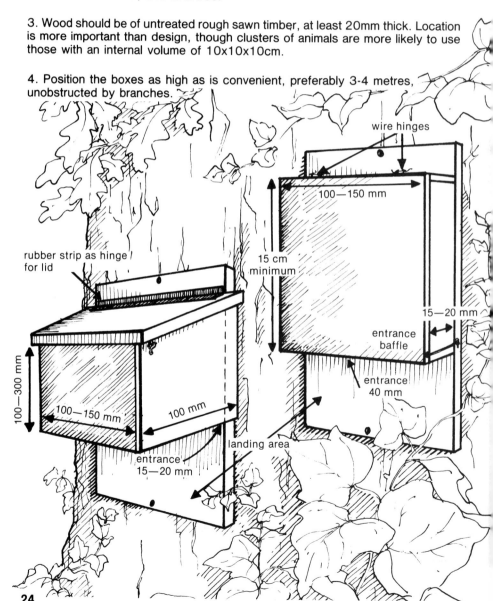

The chance of actually finding bats in boxes is less than 1 in 10. The presence of droppings counts as success, showing that bats are taking advantage of what you have provided. Bird droppings can look similar, but have white uric acid at one end, and are usually grouped in one or two circles at the bottom of the box. Bat droppings are dark and crumbly with no white part, and are irregularly scattered.

When inspecting boxes, open carefully and do not attempt to handle bats that you find. **If you plan a large project, please contact the local bat group for advice and inform them of any success you have**, noting date, weather conditions, design and position of box.

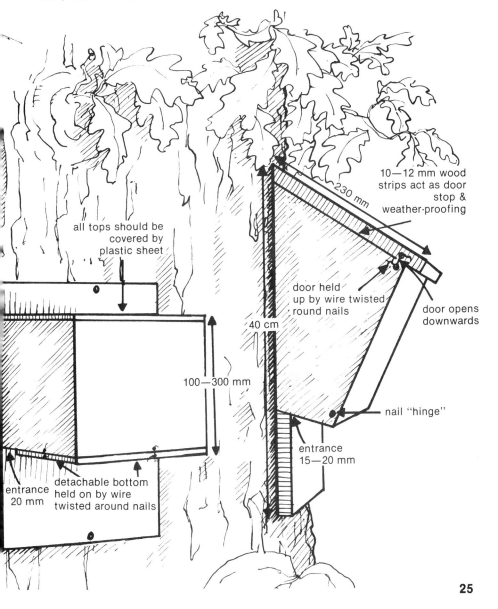

10—12 mm wood strips act as door stop & weather-proofing

230 mm

all tops should be covered by plastic sheet

door held up by wire twisted round nails

door opens downwards

40 cm

100—300 mm

nail "hinge"

entrance 15—20 mm

entrance 20 mm

detachable bottom held on by wire twisted around nails

8. Beyond the Garden Wall

Bat Conservation

Man's boundaries are different from those recognised by wildlife. To survive successfully bats must fly beyond the garden wall. As public concern over environmental problems grows, there are more opportunities to increase awareness of our wildlife.

On a large-scale map of your neighbourhood mark potential feeding grounds and open water. Try to discover whether bats *are* seen in these areas. Are there mature trees suitable for roosting, caves and tunnels that might be used for hibernation? Is there any threat of clearance or development?

Try to encourage a greater awareness among planners and councils of the importance of safeguarding wildlife habitats. Many have official strategies and are open to suggestions. Felling of trees should be avoided whenever possible, and any potential feeding or roosting site threatened with destruction should be looked at within a wider context. Many planning applications are studied in isolation, but an important link could be broken by the loss of a single site. Your map could help, especially if bat sightings and roosts are marked.

By reducing the use of weedkillers, or timing the cutting of roadside verges more carefully, very positive improvements can be made. Try to persuade local councils and park keepers to reserve unmanicured areas for wildlife, and to plant only *native* trees.

More may be gained by combining with others, so join your county **Wildlife Trust** or **Urban Wildlife Group**.

Bats and the law

The **Wildlife and Countryside Act, 1981, gives protection to all British bats and their roosts.** It is an offence to intentionally damage, destroy or obstruct access to any place that a bat uses for shelter, including houses and outbuildings. It is also illegal to deliberately kill, disturb or handle a wild bat unless licensed to do so.

The **Nature Conservancy Council (NCC) must be consulted** if any building work or remedial timber treatment is planned at any site used by bats. Advice will then be given on the most suitable treatment and timing, based on an assessment by a trained person.

Occasionally a bat enters a living area, and it is perfectly legal to remove such a visitor. Turn off the room lights, and open the windows wide, or if at rest take it gently in a gloved hand and release immediately. Should an *injured* bat be found, it is legal to tend it in order to release it to the wild, but this is specialist work and you are strongly advised to contact your local bat group.

Get in touch with your local bat group or NCC office if you are not certain what to do in any of the above situations.

9. Activities and Investigations

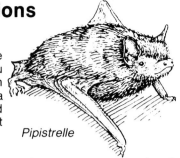

Pipistrelle

Colony Surveys

If you have bats roosting in your house, or the home of an interested relation or neighbour, you can gather a good deal of interesting information by watching them regularly, especially if it is a nursery roost. Note the dates of first arrivals and last departures, as bats will normally be present only in summer.

It is important not to disturb bats, and that lofts used as roosts are not entered unnecessarily by unlicenced people. Suggestions are given here for investigations that can take place *without* disturbance. To ensure an accurate record keep a notebook to jot down numbers and observations on behaviour *at the time*.

Stand **quietly** outside the roost site just before it gets dark. Never shine your torch at the bats.

1. Record date, weather, time of sunset and the exact time the first bat leaves the roost. Count the bats as they emerge, and note the time the last one leaves.

2. Record how many bats emerge in each five minute period. It will probably take between half an hour and an hour for them all to come out. Make a chart or graph of the numbers of bats you have seen, and a sketch of where they emerge.

3. Count in the same way regularly, for example, every night for a week, or once a week or fortnight through June, July and August. Note how the pattern changes during that time.

By regularly watching a nursery colony, you can build up a clearer picture of the colony's behaviour, especially if you can do this every year. Does the colony stay here all the season? If not, can you find out where they go? Sometimes a colony will use several houses in a road. What seems to make them move? What date do the highest number of adults appear to be present? Can you work out when the young are born? How does the emergence pattern change at this time? When do the young first fly? What do you notice about them?

Please tell your **local Bat Group** about 'your' colony and what you are doing. They may be able to visit and confirm indentification.

A national annual bat colony survey began in 1978, organised by the Institute of Terrestrial Ecology. Throughout Britain some householders with nursery colonies in their houses count the bats each year as they emerge on 2 or 3 warm evenings in June. By gathering all this information together, a picture is given of colony sizes, changes in populations, and regional and annual differences. More counts are needed in all parts of the country, so please take part if you can. I.T.E.'s address is given in Appendix C.

Noctule

Bat Watching

The study of a mere 15 species of bat sounds comparatively simple, but in fact bat-watching is both fascinating and challenging.

Plans must be laid carefully. First choose a warm, calm summer evening. Cover up as much bare skin as possible, whatever the temperature, as a good batting night is a good insect night! Find a place known to be frequented by bats, or that has all the signs of being right — edge of woodland, near water, or over pasture. Station yourself quietly before it starts to get dark.

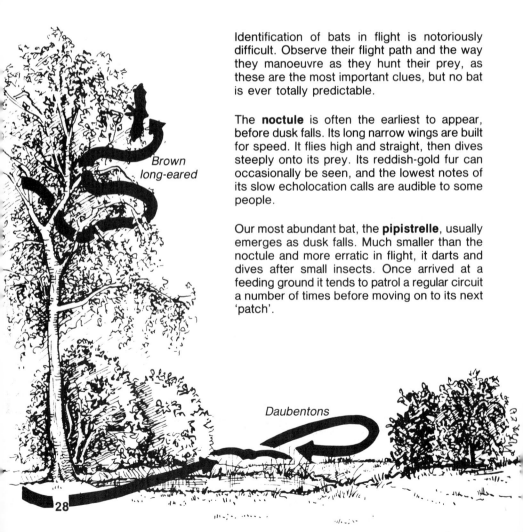

Brown long-eared

Daubentons

Identification of bats in flight is notoriously difficult. Observe their flight path and the way they manoeuvre as they hunt their prey, as these are the most important clues, but no bat is ever totally predictable.

The **noctule** is often the earliest to appear, before dusk falls. Its long narrow wings are built for speed. It flies high and straight, then dives steeply onto its prey. Its reddish-gold fur can occasionally be seen, and the lowest notes of its slow echolocation calls are audible to some people.

Our most abundant bat, the **pipistrelle**, usually emerges as dusk falls. Much smaller than the noctule and more erratic in flight, it darts and dives after small insects. Once arrived at a feeding ground it tends to patrol a regular circuit a number of times before moving on to its next 'patch'.

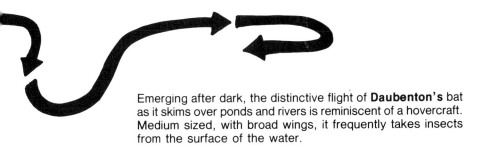

Emerging after dark, the distinctive flight of **Daubenton's** bat as it skims over ponds and rivers is reminiscent of a hovercraft. Medium sized, with broad wings, it frequently takes insects from the surface of the water.

The **brown long-eared bat** frequently gleans moths from leaves, flying silently and slowly in and out of the branches, sometimes even hovering, on its broad wings. At times its enormous ears may be glimpsed.

Watch for differences in size, flight and behaviour, and record all these, even if uncertain of species. Notes taken at the time may have more meaning later. Record dates too, as behaviour varies through the seasons. Mothers and juveniles may be seen flying together in late July and August, while autumn is the best time to watch social behaviour when mating takes place. **Please pass on observations to your local bat group.**

Most of the sounds emitted by bats while foraging for food are ultrasonic, and therefore outside human hearing. The use of a bat detector, which artificially reduces the frequency of these ultrasonic sounds, can add an exciting new dimension to batwatching. Bats may be 'heard' when it is hard to see them, and while records based on bat detectors are not officially accepted, some models can give an extra clue to identification.

Pipistrelle

Looking at Churches

Many churches are important roosting sites for bats, though despite the myth, the main body of the church and the porch are usually preferred to the belfry. Searching churches for evidence of bats during the summer months can build up a useful picture of general distribution of bats in the neighbourhood. Alternatively, regular checking of one church where bats are known to be present provides a clearer pattern of its seasonal use.

Signs to look for

Droppings. These are small and dark mouse-like droppings but crumble readily to dust. Shiny undigested insect parts may be seen through a magnifier. Colour, shape and size vary according to species. You are most likely to find signs of pipistrelles, but two or three species may use the same church.
Check porches, floor, pews, window-sills, and ledges, preferably just *before* the cleaner is due. Scattered droppings indicate where bats have been flying. Accumulations of droppings high on the wall, or on the floor, are clues to the actual roosting site.

Looking for feeding signs. Concentrations of moth or beetle wings may indicate a favourite feeding perch for a long-eared bat.

Access. Try to find out where bats enter and leave the church. Droppings beneath and on the door will suggest that they use the crack above it. They may use a gap at the eaves or some exit high in the roof. Once this is established, a colony can be monitored. (See page 27.)

Churchyards are often used as regular feeding grounds, being sheltered by trees and walls, and are worth watching at dusk. Many are now actively managed for wildlife.

Important.

Please respect the church and churchyard and ask permission from the vicar before undertaking detailed studies. The church officials may not be aware of the importance of their church as a roost site. If remedial or repair work is planned, the Nature Conservancy Council should be informed.

Droppings can be a nuisance in a church, so have sympathy with the cleaners. It often helps to emphasise the seasonal nature of this problem, and the harmlessness of the droppings.

Your local bat group may be planning or already doing a survey in the county and would welcome your help. Please contact them first if you would like to study your area.

10. Further Activities

Suitable for children, schools and other groups.

A Neighbourhood Bat Map.

With the help of an Ordnance Survey map draw a large scale plan of your neighbourhood. Mark in roads and blocks of houses, trees, hedges and water. On it note any bat sightings made by you or your friends and neighbours. Fix on a wall, and use pin-flags as numbered markers. Make a key and record details of each sighting — time, date, weather, sunset, wind, temperature, map reference. If you know of any roosts, mark those in a different way. (See page 27 for roost survey ideas.) Try to find feeding areas. Carefully observe bats over lake, field or parkland. Is there more than one species? Ask you local bat group if they can help you identify them. Gradually build up a better picture of your neighbourhood bats.

Understanding echolocation

When riding as passenger in a car through a built-up area, sit by an open window, listening to the changes in sound as you pass by walls, trees and fences, or under bridges. Close your eyes as you drive along a familiar route, and try to identify land marks by sound.

More about echoes. Try to obtain a metal clicker toy. Basically a thin strip of sprung steel with a dent in the middle, these make sharp clicks when pressed. Held in cupped hands out-of-doors, distinct echoes can be received from walls and large trees, and much experimenting can be done.

Search for your supper — A game about echolocation. Seat a group in a circle with one blindfolded child, the 'Bat', in the centre with a pointer. The leader quietly chooses an 'Insect' from the circle. Each time the Bat clicks, the Insect makes the same number of clicks, imitating echoes. The bat points to where he thinks the insect is. The more clicks there are, the more accurate the Bat. This game could be developed by spreading the group out more, or by introducing two species of Bat with different clicking signals searching for two different prey species.

A Bat Anthology

Make a collection of poetry and prose that refers to bats. How did the writer feel about bats? What were those feelings based on? Collect myths about bats, both from books and from hearsay. Are they based on fact? How do you think they originated? Are they true? Add your own poetry and prose about bats expressing your feelings towards them.

Bats and numbers.

Pipistrelles can eat over 3,000 insects in a night. What do 3,000 insects look like? Using small seeds or beads, count out piles in 10s, then 50s, until the group has build up 3,000. **How big are British bats?** Draw life-size outlines of them, noting too their different wing-shapes. **How heavy are the different British species?** Compare these weights with some common objects, such as paper-clips or 1p coins.

Topics to follow up

Much of the information needed to help with these topics may be found in books listed in Appendix A.

Find out more about bats in Britain. All British bats eat insects. Can you discover which insects are preferred by different species? Find out the insects they need as food. At what time of the year can these insects be found, and what do they in turn depend upon to survive? Work out the food chains involved. Make a calendar of insect availability, and look around to see what gaps there may be in your neighbourhood.

A Bat Habitat Scrapbook

Take photographs or cut out pictures from magazines of the sort of places that bats prefer to hunt for food. Remember that different species will hunt in different places, and that all need water to drink. Collect pictures of places they might choose to roost. This will vary through the year and with species, so try to work out when each may be used and by which bats. (There is still much we do not know.) Use the picture on the centre pages to give you ideas.

Make a **Bad News for Bats** section in your scrapbook. Put into it picture of things that reduce opportunities for bats feeding and roosting — from photographs of trees felled for development to advertisements for insecticides.

Bats Worldwide

There are nearly a thousand species of bat in the world. Although they all belong to the order *Chiroptera,* they can be divided into two very different sub-orders, the **Megachiroptera** and the **Microchiroptera.** Find out about the differences between them. Using a map of the world, find out where different bats live. What habitats do they need and what food do they eat?

Many are very important to man because they pollinate useful trees and shrubs, or help spread their seeds. Among the valuable fruits, nuts and spices at least partly dependent on bats are bananas, cashew nuts, vanilla, mangoes and figs. Try to add to the list, and make a collection of these products or pictures of them.

Collect or copy pictures of flowers visited by bats; how are the bats and flowers helping each other? How else are bats useful to man?

Numbers of bats are declining throughout the world. Many are killed needlessly because of misunderstanding. Find out how man is endangering bats in other countries. Think particularly about destruction of their habitats.

Crafty Bats

There are many ways of using bats in pictures, friezes, decorations and greetings cards. Try some of these ideas.

Make a Batmobile. Cut out bat shapes — they may be the same, or several species — and hang singly or in a group against a plain background. An alternative mobile could represent a food chain, a single bat at the top, and insects on which it feeds hanging below. Different species of 'top bat' would have different species of insect as prey.

Make a night and day frieze. Painted or made of cut-outs, daytime might be in colour, showing places where bats roost. Silhouettes can show bats feeding as darkness falls.

Make a collage of a bat garden using a wide range of textures — fabrics, wallpaper, rubbings, natural materials — to represent features that would attract bats.

Make drawings of bats. Use photographs and identification keys to make sure that details are correct. (For instance, notice the *tragus* of the long-eared bat on page 7 is quite a different shape to that of the noctule on page 8.)

Make a collage map or aerial view of an actual or a fictional place, showing roosting sites and feeding grounds for bats. Use a mixture of textures, textiles, papers, and anything else that helps add a third dimension.

Cut-out shapes. Cut-out bat shapes can be used to depict bats emerging from a roost. A long folded strip will make a hanging bat decoration (like 'dancing dollies'). A square folded and cut carefully creates a circle of bats.

Christmas and Birthday cards. These are fun both to make and receive. There are endless possibilities — bats pulling Father Christmas' sleigh, batty decorations on the Christmas tree or cake, — and many more. The entire card could be in the shape of folded bat's wings, or bats might pop up in the centre.

Hallowe'en decorations might include streamers of crepe paper with potato-printed bat shapes. Hanging bat shapes and bat masks all fit into the Hallowe'en scene — but mind you make them *friendly* bats!

Search for bat motifs and designs in old paintings and patterns, early Egyptian designs, heraldry and carvings of other cultures. In China the bat is a symbol of happiness and a bearer of good fortune. Chinese ceramics frequently depict bats, often very stylised, with wings outspread. Use bat shapes as a basis for your own abstract designs, in paint, embroidery or some other medium.

Appendix A — SELECTED BOOK LIST

Books on bats

Given below are the more recent books written on bats. It is always interesting to read older ones, especially accounts based on observations by early naturalists, but bear in mind that some of the information in these may be incorrect. For example, the use of ultrasonic sound for echolocation was not understood until the late 1930s, and new facts are still being discovered. Bats are difficult animals to study, and only in the last few years has new technology enabled us to use such gadgets as bat detectors, image intensifiers, radio tags and high speed cameras to help reveal more about their way of life.

Althea Braithwaite 1985, **Bats,** Longman, Essex (Life Cycle Books) — for children
Allen, E. 1987, **Max and the Birthday Bat,** Hodder & Stoughton — a story book for children
Haffner & Stutz, 1989, **A Family of Bats,** A & C Black — for children
Hill J.E. & Smith J.M. 1984, **Bats. A Natural History.** British Museum. (Nat Hist)
Hines J&M. 1986, **The Secret World of Bats,** Methuen, London
Hutson, A.M. 1987, **Bats in Houses,** Mammal Society, London
A more detailed look at the features of houses used as roost sites, with suggestions of how to develop these. Species accounts are also included.
Richardson, P.W. 1985, **Bats,** Whittet Books, London.
A very readable account of British bats, written to appeal to adults and to older children. An ideal introduction to bat study.
Schober, W. 1984, **The Lives of Bats,** Croom Helm, Kent
Stebbings, R.E. 1986, **Which Bat Is It?** Mammal Society (available from School Garden Co.)
Stebbings, R.E. 1986, **Bats,** Anthony Nelson, Shropshire (Mammal Society Series.)
Stebbings, R.E. 1988, **The Conservation of European Bats,** Christopher Helm, London.
Stebbings, R.E. & Walsh, S. 1985, **Bat Boxes,** Mammal Society, London
A new enlarged edition of the earlier booklet on the history, function construction and use of bats boxes in the conservation of bats
Wardhaugh, A.A. 1987, **Bats of the British Isles,** Shire Publications, Bucks.

Wildlife Gardening

Baines, C. 1985, **How to make a Wildlife Garden,** Guild Publishing. Practical advice on developing a wildlife garden, either starting from scratch or adapting an existing garden. (Available from School Garden Co.)

Cawdell, P. 1987, **Starting a Butterfly Garden,** School Garden Company. By incorporating these ideas, you could have butterflies by day as well as bats by night!

Sibley, Peter 1989 **Starting a Wildlife Pond,** School Garden Company. A detailed, practical guide for homes and schools.

Appendix B — RESOURCES

Slide-pack: 'Focus on Bats', Stebbings, R.E. & Hutson, A.M. 1984.
Fauna & Flora Preservation Society, London/International Centre for Conservation Education, Cheltenham. 40 slides with commentary booklet.

A **Bat Project Pack** for schools. Stirchley Grange Environmental Centre, Stirchley, Telford, Shropshire.

Bats A chart and notes for schools. Pictorial Charts Educational Trust, available from School Garden Co.

The Young Batworker A termly newsletter for childern enthusiastic about bats. Available free on receipt of a stamped addressed envelope from:
The Editor, 5 Manor Road, Tankerton, Whitstable, Kent CT5 2JT.